Stringpops 1

fun pieces for absolute beginners

VIOLIN/CELLO & PIANO

Peter Wilson
String parts edited by Madeleine Ranger

Illustrations by Penny Dann

Faber Music Limited

London

1. Open String Samba

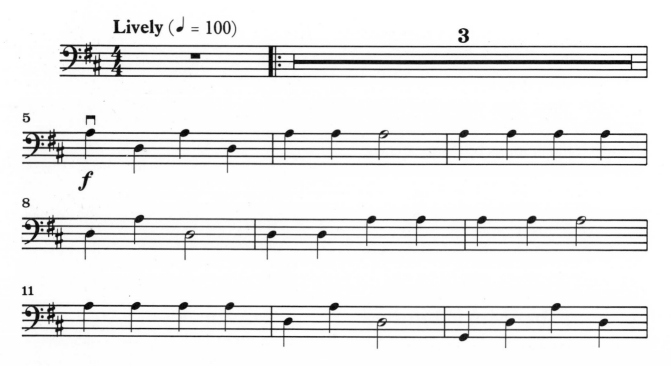

2. Calypso

3. March of the Cadets

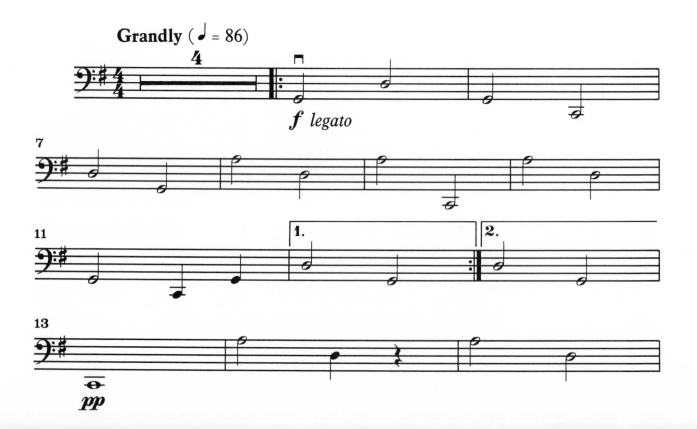

4. Bow Rock

5. Piccadilly Ballad

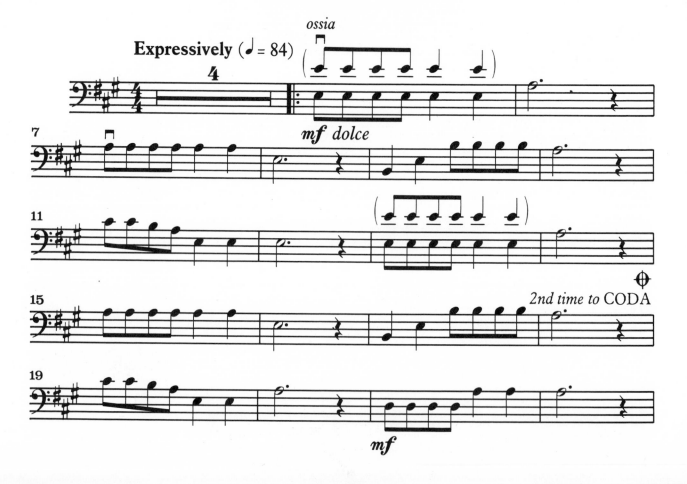

6. Jazz Waltz

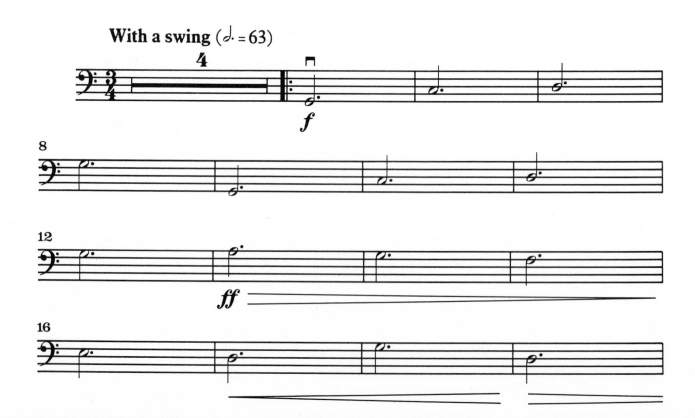

7. Sky Diver

Reproduced and printed by Halstan & Co. Ltd., Amersham, Bucks., England